FUN WITH FOOD

Contents

Simon Cheshire

Story illustrated by
Pet Gotohda

Find out about

• Different foods all over the world

Tricky words

• vegetarians
• blood
• stomach
• goanna
• dolphin
• witchetty
• termites

Introduce these tricky words and help the reader when they come across them later!

Text starter

People all over the world choose different things to eat. Some people like to eat lizard, and others like to eat cow's stomach! Would you eat kangaroo or snake? Some people even eat insects!

Weird Food

What food do you like to eat?
When you go shopping, do you
like to choose things to put in
the shopping trolley?
All over the world, people choose
different kinds of food to eat.

Do you like to eat meat?
All over the world people eat different kinds of meat.
But many people do not eat meat at all. They are called vegetarians.

England

In England, some people like to eat black pudding – that's made with the blood of animals!
Would you eat that?

South America

In South America, some people like to eat tripe – that's made from the stomach of a cow!

Australia

In Australia, some people like to eat goanna – that's a kind of lizard. And some people like to eat kangaroo. What do you think kangaroo tastes like?

Korea

In Korea, some people like to eat bird's nest soup!
They say it tastes very nice.
Would you eat that?

China

In China, some people like to eat snake.
What do you think snake tastes like?

Iceland

In Iceland, some people like to eat dolphin. And some people like to eat raw shark! They put the shark in the ground and three months later they dig it up, dry it, and then eat it! They say it tastes very nice.

Eating Bugs!

Would you eat a bug?
You might think it is very odd
to eat a bug but some insects are
good for you.

DRY ROASTED ANTS

BUG CRUNCH

Would you like to crunch on a grasshopper or swallow some ants?

In Australia, some people like to eat witchetty grubs. They say the grubs have a sweet taste.

Some people eat them raw.
Some people barbecue them.
You can even buy witchetty grub soup!

All over the world, there are many different insects to eat:

- caterpillars
- termites
- locusts
- spiders

And many different ways to cook them – boiled, roasted or fried.

Do you think eating insects is gross? Well, you may have eaten some!

Insects can get into food when it is made. There may even be tiny pieces of insect in your bar of chocolate!

Likes and Dislikes

People like to eat different foods. Some people like some things but other people hate them.

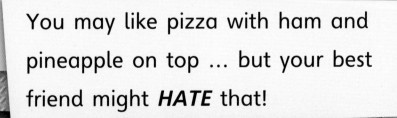

You may like pizza with ham and pineapple on top ... but your best friend might *HATE* that!

Your best friend might like to eat
a peanut butter and jam sandwich ...
but you might *HATE* that!

Some people like to eat funny things together.
You might like fish.
You might like chocolate.
But would you eat fish with chocolate?

You might like ice cream.
But would you eat it with snails?

Quiz

Text Detective

- What do vegetarians not eat?
- What is your favourite food?

Word Detective

- **Phonic Focus:** Adding 'ing' to words ending with e
  Page 12: Which letter must be dropped from
  'hate' before adding 'ing'?
- Page 4: Why does the word 'England' start
  with a capital letter?
- Page 7: Find a word meaning 'uncooked'.

Super Speller

Read these words:

hating   later   choose

Now try to spell them!

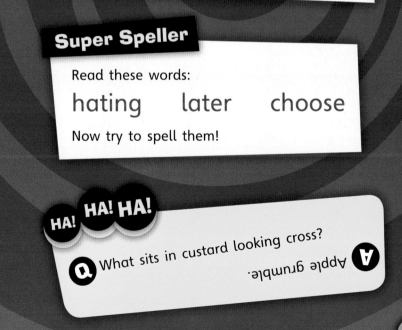

HA! HA! HA!

Q What sits in custard looking cross?

A Apple grumble.

15

In this story

 Ziggy

 Pod

 Checkout lady

Tricky words

- mission
- costume
- trolley
- sign
- obey
- pieces

Introduce these tricky words and help the reader when they come across them later!

Story starter

Ziggy and Pod are aliens. They have been sent to Earth to find out how humans live. Today, their mission is to find out how Earth people go shopping, so they go to a supermarket.

Aliens at the Supermarket

Ziggy and Pod had dressed up as humans.

"Our mission today is to find out about Earth shopping," said Ziggy.

"OK, boss," said Pod.

Ziggy and Pod went to the supermarket.
"Is my human costume OK?" asked Pod.
"I have got one head, two legs and
four arms."

"You fool!" said Ziggy.

"How many times have I told you? Humans have one head, two legs and *two* arms."

"Sorry, boss," said Pod.

"We must have human names so that we fit in," said Ziggy. Pod looked around.

WELCOME TO SUPERSAVE!

"I know, boss," he said, "you can be called Mr Supersave, and I can be called Mrs Supersave."

Ziggy and Pod saw each human take a trolley into the supermarket. "What is that cage on wheels?" asked Pod.

"I don't know," said Ziggy, "but we must do what humans do."

"Look!" said Ziggy. "Humans feed their cages with food."

"That human is feeding her baby to the cage," said Pod.

"That's why the baby is crying," said Ziggy.

"Good thinking, boss," said Pod.

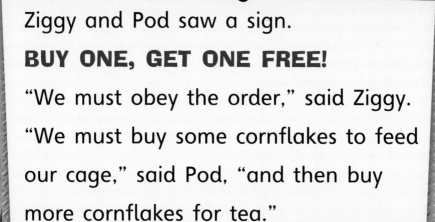

Ziggy and Pod saw a sign.

BUY ONE, GET ONE FREE!

"We must obey the order," said Ziggy.

"We must buy some cornflakes to feed our cage," said Pod, "and then buy more cornflakes for tea."

Ziggy and Pod saw another sign.

3 FOR 2

"What does it mean?" said Pod.

"There are *two* of us," said Ziggy. "So it must mean we have to take *three* tins of beans."

They saw another sign.

36 SORTS OF CHEESE!

TRY THEM ALL!

"That is a lot of cheese," said Pod.

"We must obey the order," said Ziggy.

"Take all the cheese."

"Good! Now we have got food for tea," said Ziggy. "We will eat cornflakes and beans, with cheese on top."

"We will be just like real humans," said Pod.

At the checkout they saw a man hand over some pieces of paper.

"Did you see that?" said Ziggy.
"Humans just give paper for the food."
"And the human took the cage too!" said Pod.

Ziggy took some pieces of paper out of their kitbag.

"Is this all you need?" said Ziggy.

"Yes," said the lady. "Thank you."

"Humans are so silly," said Ziggy.
"We have all this food and a free cage,
and we just gave them some paper."

Ziggy and Pod went back to their spaceship to write their mission report.

What do you think of Pod's cooking?

MISSION REPORT TO HOME PLANET

Visit to Supermarket

Humans have to obey signs.

They have to feed cages with food.

They swap paper for the food.

Then they take the cage away.

Humans are so silly.

Quiz

- Why did Ziggy and Pod take all the cheese?
- Which misunderstanding did you think was the funniest?

Word Detective

- **Phonic Focus**: Adding 'ing' to words ending with e
  Page 25: Which letter must be dropped from 'take' before adding 'ing'?
- Page 21: What words does Ziggy say?
- Page 27: Find a word made from two words.

Super Speller

Read these words:

taking   shopping   sorry

Now try to spell them!

HA! HA! HA!

Q What is an alien's favourite sweet?

A Martian-mallows.